THIS JOURNAL

BELONGS TO:

....

This workbook is intended to help you control your thoughts and reflect on your practices. Many athletes have talent, but the greats have a **strong mental game** that propels them to the top. What are you willing to do to get to the next level?

Who is your favorite athlete?

. . . .

When the game is on the line, how
do they act?
What is their response to failure?
Do they quit, throw a fit, or move on?

Now, what about you?

What is your body language like?
What do you think /feel
when the game is on the line?
What do you do when things do
not go your way?

_____

_____

_____

_____

_____

_____

BE HONEST:
WHAT ARE YOUR STRENGTHS & WEAKNESSES AS A SOFTBALL PLAYER?

Strengths	Weaknesses

Training is tough.

What will you say to yourself
to keep you inspired?
Create a catch phrase below
that will encourage you when
you're down.

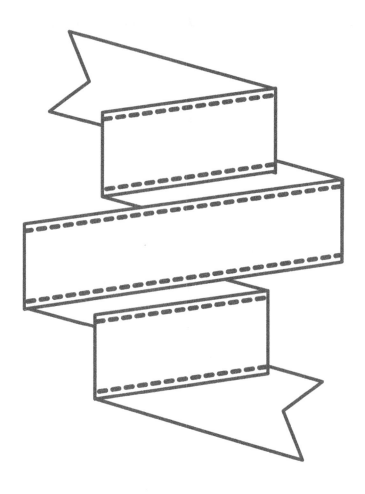

TALKING TO YOURSELF

What you say matters.

What do you sound like when you talk
to yourself? Is it kind? Is it negative?
Does it help you....or hurt you?

What positive things do you say to yourself?	What negative things do you say to yourself?

I am going to share some of my negative
thoughts with you from when I played,
so that you know you are not alone and it is normal.
Everyone defaults to negative thoughts. It is easier.

"I suck!"
"I let my teammates down."
"I can't hit today."
"What if I make a throwing error?"
Worried I will strike out

None of these thoughts helped me play better
or feel better. They served no purpose and in fact,
only hurt my performance. Have you had
a similar experience?

Your brain is a computer
and it tells your
body what to do.
What you think
influences the outcome.

What happens when we think the following:

"Don't swing at the change up"

Outcome: you'll swing at the change up

"Lay off the high pitch."

Outcome: you'll swing at the high pitch

"Don't strike out."

Outcome: Likely to strike out

WHY DOES THIS HAPPEN?

Our brains are not capable of picturing
negatives. For example if I say:
"DON'T picture a blue striped penguin"
What do you see?

Most likely you'll see a blue striped penguin
All your brain hears is blue striped penguin.
It ignores the don't.
How can we make our
thoughts more productive?

LET'S REFRAME

HOW WE

THINK!

Tell your body what you want it to do!
Stay away from the word don't.
Here are some examples:

Don't swing at the high pitch.	Think low.
Don't pull my head.	Keep my head still.
Don't strike out.	Make contact/ put the ball in play.
Don't overthrow the ball.	Stay low. Follow through.

GOAL SETTING

Goal setting is important because this practice drives your training.

Let's take some time and think about what overall skills you want to improve upon this year.

Big Picture Goal Setting

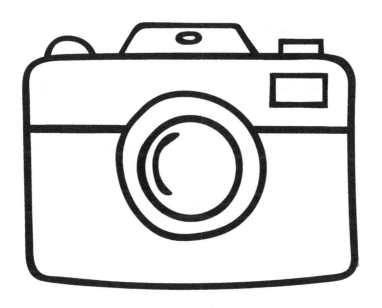

What do you want to
achieve this year?

DEFENSIVE GOALS

Be specific. Make it measurable. Achievable. Realistic.
Create a time frame.

⚾ _____

⚾ _____

⚾ _____

⚾ _____

⚾ _____

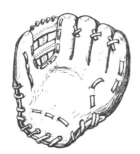

DEFENSIVE GOALS

Take your goals and dig deep! What are you willing to do right now to make progress toward that goal. (ie: practice short hops for 10 min a day.)

_____

_____

_____

_____

_____

_____

_____

_____

_____

_____

_____

_____

_____

Offensive Goals

Be specific. Make it measurable. Achievable. Realistic.
Create a time frame.

⚾ _____

⚾ _____

⚾ _____

⚾ _____

⚾ _____

Offensive Goals

Take your goals and dig deep! What are you willing
to do right now to make progress toward that goal.
(ie: Hit 3/5 line drives off of the tee. Weight lift 3x a week.)

⚾ _____

_____

_____

⚾ _____

_____

_____

⚾ _____

_____

_____

⚾ _____

_____

_____

⚾ _____

_____

_____

What if you fail?

You **are** going to fail. You will fail **many** times.
It is part of the game and even more so, it is
part of life. Do not fear failure, embrace it.

I encourage you to fail as much as you can.

Change your mindset about failure.
If you can learn from it, then failing was **worth** it.
It means you are growing. If everything is easy,
it means you are not pushing yourself.
Don't take it from me, take the advice
of one of the greats...

*"I've missed more than 9,000 shots in my career.
I've lost almost 300 games. Twenty-six times
I've been trusted to take the game-winning shot
and missed. I've failed over and over and over
again in my life. And that is why I succeed."*
-Michael Jordan

LET'S FOCUS

You have your big picture goals, but
you must zoom in! Every single time
you practice--set a goal!
For example: During tee work
you can say, "I want to hit 3 out of 5
line drives."
For throwing you can say,
"I want to hit the first baseman
in the chest in 4 out of 5 throws."

Today's target(s):

Did you meet your goal today?

If yes, what went well?
If no, what can you do
better next time?
Even if you did not meet your goal,
did you improve?

_____

_____

_____

_____

_____

_____

_____

_____

_____

_____

Today's target(s):

Did you meet your goal today?

If yes, what went well?
If no, what can you do
better next time?
Even if you did not meet your goal,
did you improve?

_____

_____

_____

_____

_____

_____

_____

_____

_____

_____

_____

Today's target(s):

Did you meet your goal today?

If yes, what went well?
If no, what can you do
better next time?
Even if you did not meet your goal,
did you improve?

_____

_____

_____

_____

_____

_____

_____

_____

_____

_____

_____

Today's target(s):

Did you meet your goal today?

If yes, what went well?
If no, what can you do
better next time?
Even if you did not meet your goal,
did you improve?

_____

_____

_____

_____

_____

_____

_____

_____

_____

_____

Today's target(s):

Did you meet your goal today?

If yes, what went well?
If no, what can you do
better next time?
Even if you did not meet your goal,
did you improve?

_____

_____

_____

_____

_____

_____

_____

_____

_____

_____

DATE: _____

Today's target(s):

Did you meet your goal today?

REFLECT

_____

_____

_____

_____

_____

_____

_____

_____

_____

_____

Today's target(s):

Did you meet your goal today?

REFLECT

_____

_____

_____

_____

_____

_____

_____

_____

_____

_____

Today's target(s):

Did you meet your goal today?

REFLECT

_____

_____

_____

_____

_____

_____

_____

_____

_____

_____

_____

Today's target(s):

Did you meet your goal today?

REFLECT

_____

_____

_____

_____

_____

_____

_____

_____

_____

_____

Today's target(s):

Did you meet your goal today?

REFLECT

_____

_____

_____

_____

_____

_____

_____

_____

_____

_____

_____

Today's target(s):

Did you meet your goal today?

REFLECT

Today's target(s):

Did you meet your goal today?

REFLECT

_____

_____

_____

_____

_____

_____

_____

_____

_____

_____

_____

Today's target(s):

Did you meet your goal today?

REFLECT

_____

_____

_____

_____

_____

_____

_____

_____

_____

_____

_____

Today's target(s):

Did you meet your goal today?

REFLECT

_____

_____

_____

_____

_____

_____

_____

_____

_____

_____

_____

TODAY'S TARGET(S):

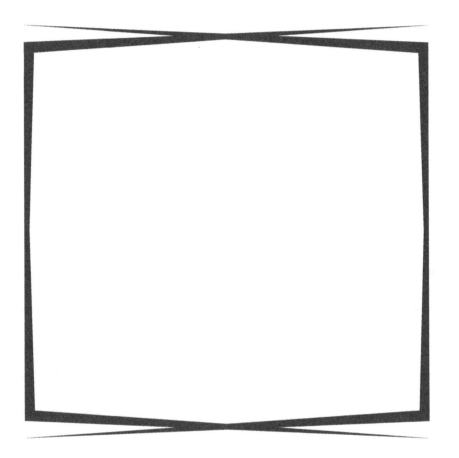

Did you meet your goal?

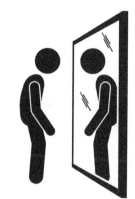

_____

_____

_____

_____

_____

_____

_____

_____

_____

_____

_____

TODAY'S TARGET(S):

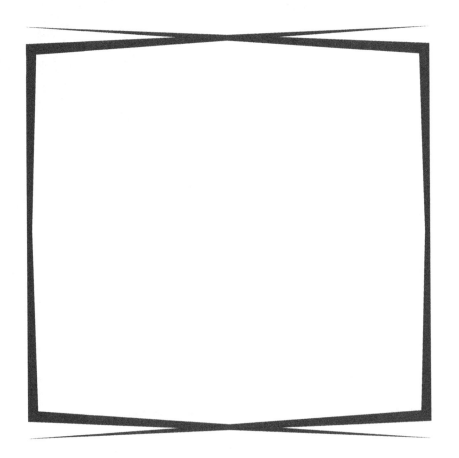

Did you meet your goal?

_____

_____

_____

_____

_____

_____

_____

_____

_____

_____

TODAY'S TARGET(S):

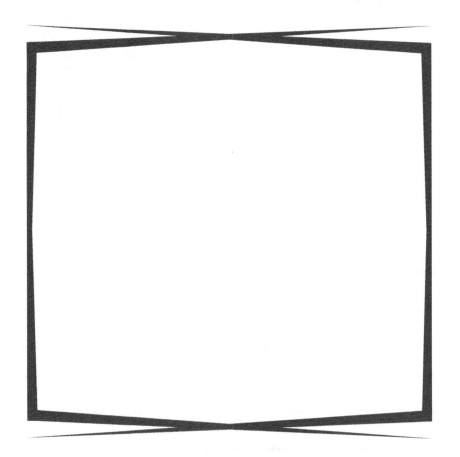

Did you meet your goal?

_____

_____

_____

_____

_____

_____

_____

_____

_____

_____

TODAY'S TARGET(S):

Did you meet
your goal?

_____

_____

_____

_____

_____

_____

_____

_____

_____

_____

TODAY'S TARGET(S):

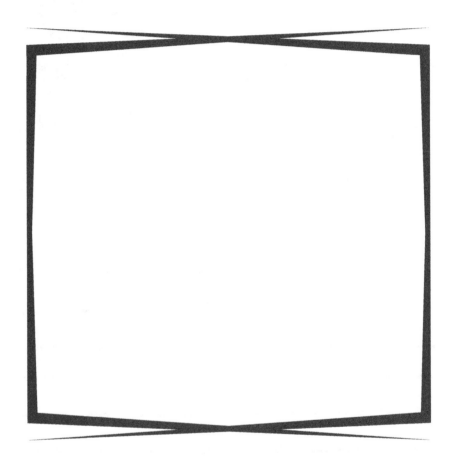

Did you meet your goal?

_____

_____

_____

_____

_____

_____

_____

_____

_____

_____

TODAY'S TARGET(S):

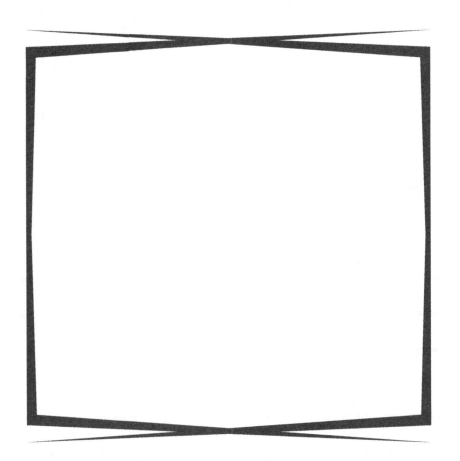

Did you meet your goal?

_____

_____

_____

_____

_____

_____

_____

_____

_____

_____

Today's Target(s):

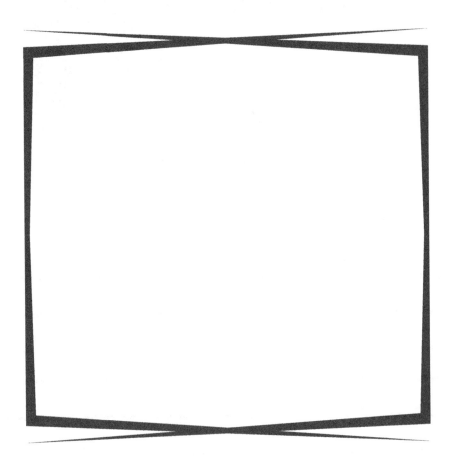

Did you meet
your goal?

_____

_____

_____

_____

_____

_____

_____

_____

_____

_____

_____

TODAY'S TARGET(S):

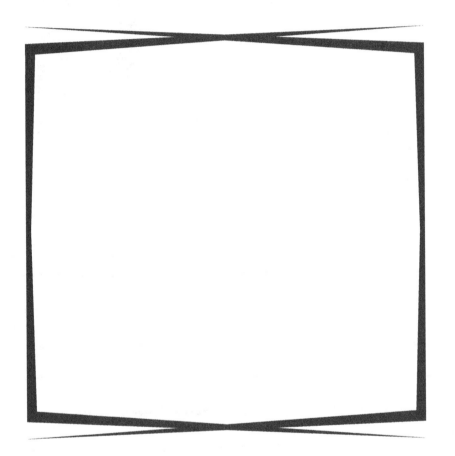

Did you meet your goal?

_____

_____

_____

_____

_____

_____

_____

_____

_____

_____

TODAY'S TARGET(S):

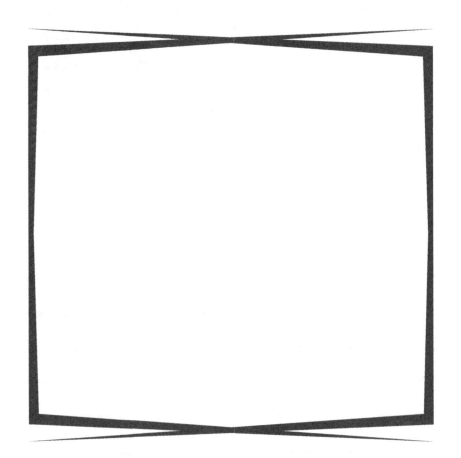

Did you meet your goal?

_____

_____

_____

_____

_____

_____

_____

_____

_____

_____

Today's Target(s):

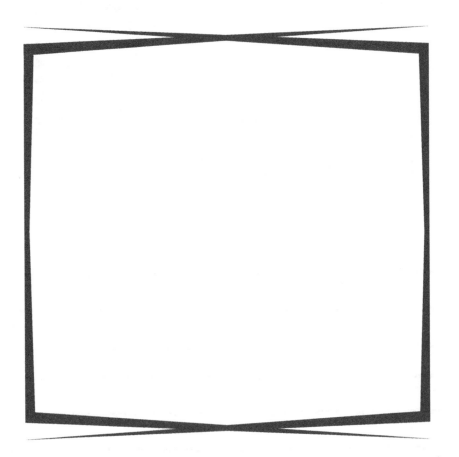

Did you meet
your goal?

Today's Target(s):

DID YOU MEET YOUR GOAL?

_____

_____

_____

_____

_____

_____

_____

_____

_____

_____

_____

Today's Target(s):

DID YOU MEET YOUR GOAL?

_____

_____

_____

_____

_____

_____

_____

_____

_____

_____

Today's Target(s):

DID YOU MEET YOUR GOAL?

_____
_____
_____
_____
_____
_____
_____
_____
_____
_____
_____

Today's Target(s):

DID YOU MEET YOUR GOAL?

Today's Target(s):

DID YOU MEET YOUR GOAL?

Today's Target(s):

DID YOU MEET YOUR GOAL?

Today's Target(s):

DID YOU MEET YOUR GOAL?

Today's Target(s):

DID YOU MEET YOUR GOAL?

_____

_____

_____

_____

_____

_____

_____

_____

_____

_____

Today's Target(s):

DID YOU MEET YOUR GOAL?

_____

_____

_____

_____

_____

_____

_____

_____

_____

_____

Today's Target(s):

DID YOU MEET YOUR GOAL?

_____

_____

_____

_____

_____

_____

_____

_____

_____

_____

DATE: _____

Today's Target(s):

DID YOU MEET YOUR GOAL?

_____

_____

_____

_____

_____

_____

_____

_____

_____

_____

_____

Today's Target(s):

DID YOU MEET YOUR GOAL?

_____

_____

_____

_____

_____

_____

_____

_____

_____

_____

DATE:

Today's Target(s):

DID YOU MEET YOUR GOAL?

Today's Target(s):

DID YOU MEET YOUR GOAL?

You are working every day to improve yourself. You should be proud. Keep up the goal setting and achieve those dreams!

Made in the USA
Monee, IL
14 July 2022